soft *c*

Nice, Nice

By Liza Charlesw

ISBN: 978-1-339-02786-9

Art Director: Tannaz Fassihi; Designer: Tanya Chernyak
Photos © Getty Images.

1 2 3 4 5 6 7 8 9 10 68 32 31 30 29 28 27 26 25 24 23

Printed in Jiaxing, China. First printing, August 2023.

See the mice on the twig.
A set of mice is
twice as nice!

Mice are NOT big.
They can fit in a hole
or a small space.

Mice are soft and cute.
See the sweet face!
See the long tail
and pink feet!

Mice like to take naps
when it’s light and bright.
They sleep in the day.

But at night, mice wake up.
Then, they jump and race
from place to place.
Creep, run, leap!

Mice eat nuts and seeds.

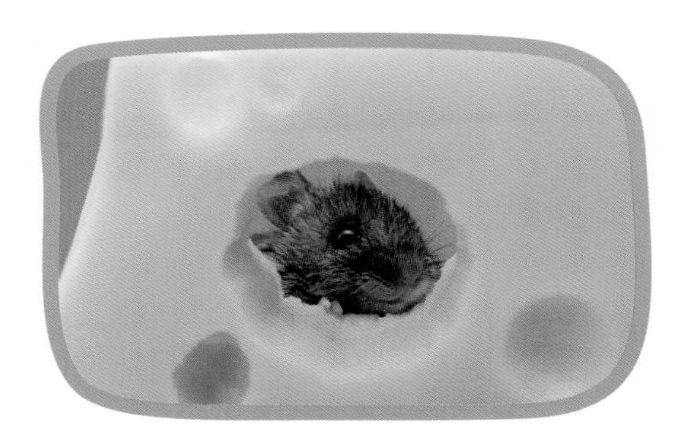

They like a slice of cheese.

See the mice on the stick.
A set of mice is
twice as nice!